Young People's Stories of Patience

*Patience is...*understanding that taking your time is sometimes better than being fast.

*Patience is...*being willing to listen, watch, and wait in order to learn.

*Patience is...*knowing that time can make a difference in what happens.

*Patience is...*thinking before you act.

Compiled by
Henry and Melissa Billings

Young People's Press
San Diego

J179.9
You

Editorial, design and production by
Book Production Systems, Inc.

Cover illustration by Randy Chewning.

Published in the United States of America.

2 3 4 5 6 7 8 9 – 99 98 97 96 95
ISBN 1-885658-42-7

Young People's

Stories of Patience

THE **IMPATIENT** MULE DRIVERS

This story comes from Mexico. It tells about how some mule owners tried to get their mules to go faster. How do you suppose patience might help people deal with animals?

Once a group of impatient mule drivers were on their way to a fair. They had sponges and hot chili peppers, which they were going to sell. The mules that carried sponges went very fast because the sponges were so light.

"That's fine," said their drivers. "We will get to the fair first and sell everything quickly. Hurry up, hurry up!"

The mules that carried the hot chili peppers didn't go so fast. "Mules are stubborn," said one driver, "but I have an idea." He took some chili peppers and rubbed them on the legs of the slow mules. This burned their legs and they began to run. They ran so fast that they left all the other animals behind.

"You certainly are clever," said the other drivers. "You will be famous some day." So all the mule drivers in the group rubbed chili peppers on their mules' legs. Off went the animals! The drivers couldn't keep up with them. The mules ran to a river and went splashing in.

As the water washed the chili off, the mules' legs stopped burning. The drivers found the mules standing on the far bank of the river, resting. The water had swelled the sponges. They were so large that everybody at the fair bought some. They looked much better than the little sponges that other groups of drivers brought. The impatient mule drivers thought they were very clever. "It takes brains to succeed in this world," they said.

With the money they got, the impatient mule drivers bought big bags of salt. "We will take these to another fair very fast and make a lot more money," they said. So the minute they started off, they rubbed chili peppers on the legs of the mules. Again the mules' legs began to burn very badly. Even though the salt they carried was very heavy, they ran like the wind. They ran and ran until they came to a deep river. They stampeded in so fast that their feet hardly touched the bottom. They snorted and snuffled and plunged around in the water until all the chili was washed off. But when the mules came out of the water, they had no packs left. The water had washed away all the salt.

The mules now felt so light and cool that the drivers couldn't catch them. The drivers ran and ran, but the animals just pranced around. From time to time they tossed

their heads and brayed cheerfully. "Awh-eee-awh!"
Then they galloped away. Even when the mules
were far away, the drivers could still hear them,
"Awh-eee-awh!"

The impatient mule drivers sat on the
ground and cried. They had lost their salt, their
money, and their mules.

The impatient mule drivers lost everything. They were not willing to take their time getting to the fair. When they saw a chance to make a lot of money, they took it. They didn't care that the chili peppers burned the legs of the mules. In the end, the drivers learned that going faster is not always the best way to go.

THE
WASP
AND THE
BEE

This story comes from Nigeria. It tells why the bee is liked by people around the world and why the wasp is not. What do you suppose patience has to do with being liked?

In the beginning, when the Creator made everything in the earth, he told the bee to go into the world. He told her how she could find things and put them together to make a honey that would sweeten everything. The Creator told the bee how to build a life that she could enjoy. The bee was very patient. She listened to all the instructions from the Creator. And then she left.

Next came the wasp's turn. The wasp was very impatient. He heard only about half of the instructions that the Creator wished to give him. Before the Creator

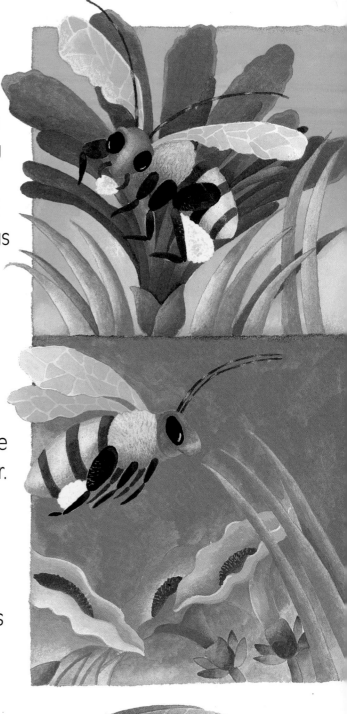

was even finished, the wasp took off, saying, "Well, I have everything I need to know."

When he got into the world, the wasp discovered that he had not received all the instructions he needed. He kept trying to make a honey, but he could not. Instead of making a honey, he made a kind of poison.

The patient bee, however, was able to put together all the things that the Creator had required her to put together. She could make a honey.

Since then, the bees have been very much liked by the people of the earth. The wasp, on the other hand, has become the enemy of all people.

This story tells about the importance of listening when someone is giving instructions. The bee listened patiently to the Creator, made honey, and became a friend to people. The wasp didn't have the patience to listen. As a result, he could make only poison, and became an enemy to people everywhere.

The LION's Whisker

This story comes from Ethiopia. Read to find out how a stepmother learned that it can take time and patience to win the trust and love of others.

Bizunesh, a woman of the African highlands, married Gudina, a man of the lowlands. Gudina had a son named Segab. Segab was very sad because his mother had died.

Bizunesh loved Segab very much and tried to be a true mother. She mended all of Segab's robes. She patched his shoes. She always asked him which food he liked best. And she always tried to save the choicest pieces of meat from the stew for Segab. But he did not thank her. He did not even speak to her.

Gudina was a merchant and was often away on business. This left Bizunesh at home alone with Segab. She spoke to him kindly. "I have always wanted a small son. Now I have one. I love you very much."

15

Bizunesh often tried to kiss her stepson. But every time she tried, Segab just ran from her. "I do not love you," he shouted. "You are not my real mother. My mother is dead."

Bizunesh often cried because of the way Segab treated her. She wished for the day when he would love her as she loved him.

One day Segab ran away from home. He stayed in the forest until his father came and found him. When Segab came home, he was especially mean to his stepmother. Bizunesh cried all that night.

The next morning, Bizunesh went to the cave of a very famous wise man. Bizunesh told him about her stepson who did not love her. She said, "You must give me a powder, one that will make Segab love me as he loved his own mother."

The wise man said, "To make such a powder I must have the chin whiskers of an old and ferocious lion who walks in the black-rock desert beyond the river. Bring the whiskers to me."

"How can I do that?" Bizunesh asked. "The lion will kill me."

"I cannot answer that," said the wise man. "I know about many things. But I know little about lions. You must find a way."

Now Bizunesh loved Segab very much. She decided that she would try to get the chin whiskers, danger or not.

Bizunesh crossed the river to the black-rock desert and looked at the lion from a safe distance. The lion was a fierce one. When he roared, Bizunesh felt afraid. She ran home.

The next day Bizunesh came from her house carrying food. She placed the food on a rock a mile away from the lion. Then she ran home.

On the following day, Bizunesh brought food and left it only a half-mile from the lion. On the next day, she left the food a quarter of a mile from the lion. She watched him from a distance while he ate.

Finally, Bizunesh left the food only a hundred yards from the fierce lion. The lion saw her and growled in a friendly way. Bizunesh stayed while the lion ate the food. The next day she left the food fifty yards from the lion.

At last Bizunesh was able to go right up to the lion and feed him. She watched the lion's great jaw fly open and crash shut! She heard the sound of his teeth tearing through the meat. She was very frightened. But she loved Segab very much. Bizunesh shut her eyes and reached out. She snatched a few whiskers from the lion's chin. The lion hardly noticed the small pain he felt. Bizunesh quickly ran back to the wise man's cave.

She was almost out of breath when she reached the cave. "I have the lion's whiskers," she cried. "Now make me the powder and Segab will surely love me."

"I will not make you any powder," the wise man said. "You learned how to approach the lion—slowly. Do the same with Segab and he will surely learn to love you."

The wise man knew that true love cannot be found in any powder. But he couldn't simply tell Bizunesh that. She needed to discover it for herself. That is why the wise man asked her to get the lion's whiskers. Segab's love was like the lion's trust. It had to be won slowly—with patience.

THE BROTHER WHO UNDERSTOOD LITTLE

This story about two brothers comes from the Jewish tradition. Read to find out what happens when one brother discovers the importance of patience and one does not.

All their lives two young brothers had lived in the city behind great stone walls. They had never seen a field or a farm. Then one day they decided to pay a visit to the country.

As they went walking along the road, they saw a farmer plowing his field. They watched him and were puzzled.

"Why on earth is he doing that?" they wondered. "He turns up the earth and leaves deep furrows in it. Why should someone take a smooth piece of land covered with nice green grass and dig it up?"

Later they watched the farmer sowing grains of wheat along the furrows. "That man must be crazy!" they exclaimed. "He takes good wheat and throws it into the dirt!"

"I don't like the country!" said the younger brother in disgust. "Only strange people live here."

So he returned to the city.

The older brother, however, decided to remain in the country. Over the next few weeks, he saw a change take place. The plowed field began to sprout tender green shoots. The shoots were much more beautiful than the grass had

been. This discovery excited him. He wrote to his brother in the city and asked him to come back at once and see the wonderful change.

The younger brother came and was delighted with what he saw. The two brothers watched the sproutings grow into golden heads of wheat. Now they both understood the purpose of the farmer's work.

When the wheat became ripe the farmer brought out his scythe and began to cut it down. Seeing this, the impatient younger brother said, "This farmer is crazy! He worked hard all these months to grow this lovely wheat. And now he is cutting it down! I'm disgusted with such an idiot! I'm going back to the city!"

The older brother, the patient one, stayed in the country. He watched the farmer gather the wheat. He saw the farmer skillfully separate the grain from the chaff. The brother was filled with wonder when he found that the farmer had harvested one hundred times as much seed as he had sowed. At last he understood everything the farmer had done.

The younger brother had no patience. When he saw the farmer doing something that seemed strange, he did not bother to try to understand it. He would not take the time to see what would happen next. The older brother, on the other hand, had the patience to see how things turned out. By staying in the country, he learned that an act of creation often takes a long time. He also grew to understand the farmer's work.

Acknowledgments

Grateful acknowledgment is made for permission to reprint the following copyrighted material:

An adaptation of "Some Impatient Mule Drivers" from THE BOY WHO COULD DO ANYTHING & OTHER MEXICAN FOLK TALES retold by Anita Brenner. © 1992 by Susannah Glusker (Linnet Books, 1992).

"The Lion's Whisker" adapted from THE LION'S WHISKER: TALES OF HIGH AFRICA by Brent Ashabranner and Russell Davis, pp. 7-9. © 1959 and 1987 by Brent Ashabranner and Russell Davis. Reprinted by permission of the authors.

"Man Understands But Little" (retitled "The Brother Who Understood Little") from A TREASURY OF JEWISH FOLKLORE edited by Nathan Ausubel. © 1948, 1976 by Crown Publishers, Inc. Reprinted by permission of Crown Publishers, Inc.

"The Wasp and the Bee," adapted for readability, from NIGERIAN FOLK TALES, Second Edition, pp. 43-44, by permission of the editors, Barbara K. and Warren S. Walker.